The Joy of American Classics

A Keyboard Panorama of our Best-loved Melodies.
Selected and edited by Denes Agay.

Foreword

The Joy of American Classics is a collection of forty-three tuneful selections written by a select group of American composers in a period ranging from colonial times to our days. The term "classics" in the title of our folio refers to the remarkably durable popularity as well as the historic and ethnic significance of the contents. In other words, by "American Classics" we mean works that stand out as distinguishable and lasting patterns in the fabric of American music, offering a wide panoramic view of our indigenous musical scene.

-Denes Agay

Cover design by Mike Bell Design

Order No. YK 20618
US International Standard Book Number: 0.8256.8089.1
UK International Standard Book Number: 0.7119.4368.0

Exclusive Distributors:
Music Sales Corporation
257 Park Avenue South, New York, New York 10010 USA
Music Sales Limited
8/9 Frith Street, London W1V 5TZ England
Music Sales Pty. Limited
120 Rothschild Street, Rosebery, Sydney, NSW 2018, Australia

Printed in the United States of America by
Vicks Lithograph and Printing Corporation

Yorktown Music Press / Music Sales Limited
London / New York / Paris / Sydney / Copenhagen / Madrid

Contents

Waltz

James Hewitt
(1770–1827)

Comfortably and gracefully

D.C. al Fine

Yankee Doodle

with Variations

Anonymous
(ca.1790)

Rondo

from the overture to the opera The Archers

Benjamin Carr
(1768–1831)

D.C. al Fine

Le Bananier

Louis Moreau Gottschalk
(1829-1869)

Con moto (♩ = 96)

Creole Eyes

Danse Cubaine

Louis Moreau Gottschalk

Lively (♩ = 84)

Country Dance

from the light opera Robin Hood

Reginald De Koven
(1859–1920)

Lively, robust waltz tempo (♩. = 66)

The Stars and Stripes Forever

John Philip Sousa
(1854–1932)

Bright, energetic march tempo (♩ = 102)

By the Waters of Minnetonka

Moon Deer

J.M. Cavanass

Slowly, tenderly

Thurlow Lieurance
(1878–1963)

D.C. al Fine

Narcissus

Elthelbert Nevin
(1862–1901)

Graceful, walking tempo

Gondoliers

from A Day in Venice

Ethelbert Nevin

To a Wild Rose

from Woodland Sketches

Edward MacDowell
(1860–1908)

The Entertainer

Scott Joplin
(1868–1917)

Fine

D.C. al Fine

Maple Leaf Rag

Scott Joplin

D.C. al Fine

Juba Dance

from In the Bottoms

Robert Nathaniel Dett
(1882–1943)

Allegro non troppo

D.C. al Fine

Nola

Felix Arndt
(1889–1918)

D.C. al Fine

Turkey in the Straw

Fiddle tune

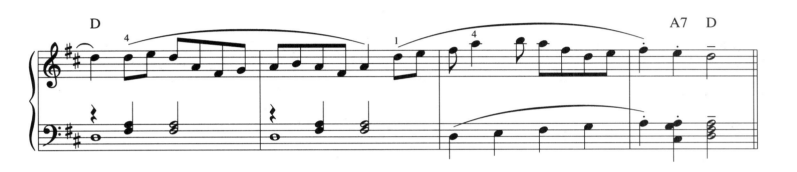

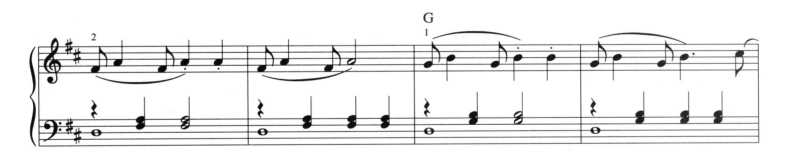

Oh! Susanna

Stephen Foster
(1826–1864)

The Old Folks at Home

Moderately

Stephen Foster

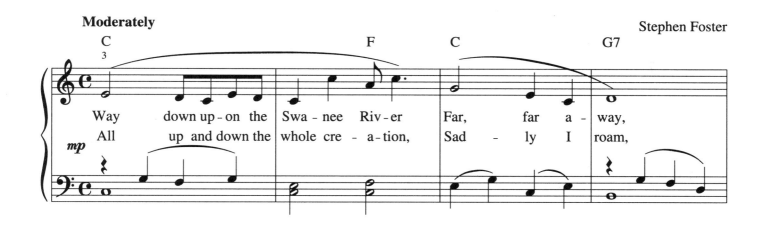

Way   down up-on the   Swa - nee Riv-er   Far,   far a - way,
All   up and down the   whole cre - a-tion,   Sad - ly   I   roam,

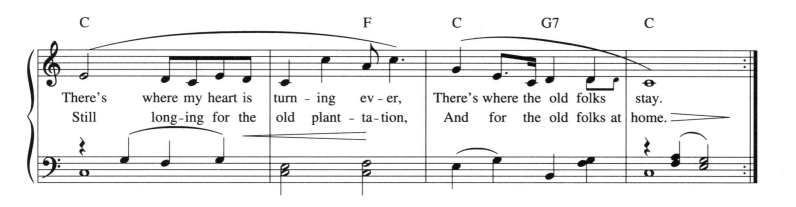

There's   where my heart is   turn - ing ev-er,   There's where the old folks   stay.
Still   long-ing for the   old plant - ta-tion,   And   for   the old folks at   home.

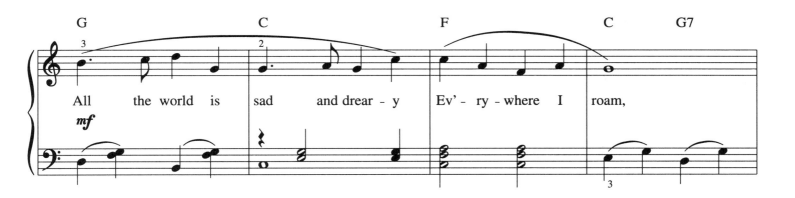

All   the world is   sad   and drear - y   Ev' - ry - where   I   roam,

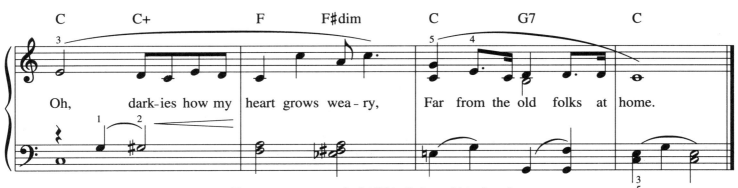

Oh,   dark-ies how my   heart grows wea - ry,   Far from the old   folks   at   home.

Beautiful Dreamer

Moderately

Stephen Foster

Battle Hymn of the Republic

Julia Ward Howe

Traditional

America, the Beautiful

Katherine L. Bates
Moderately

Samuel Augustus Ward
(1906–1960)

O beau - ti - ful for spa - cious skies, For am - ber waves of grain, For

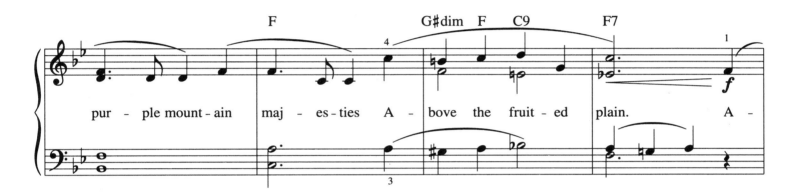

pur - ple mount - ain maj - es - ties A - bove the fruit - ed plain. A -

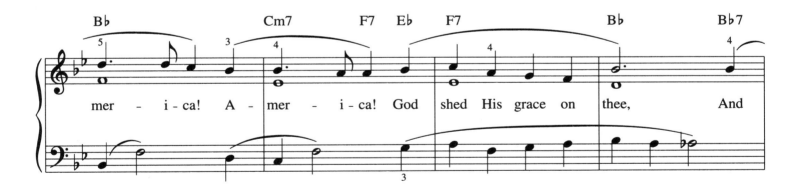

mer - i - ca! A - mer - i - ca! God shed His grace on thee, And

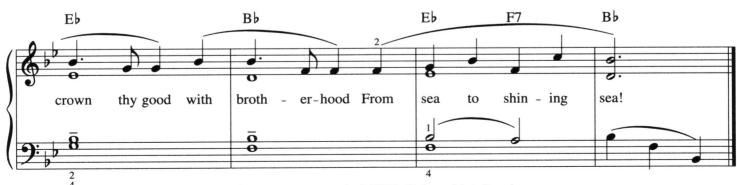

crown thy good with broth - er-hood From sea to shin - ing sea!

Swing Low, Sweet Chariot

Spiritual

Nobody Knows the Trouble I've Seen

Spiritual

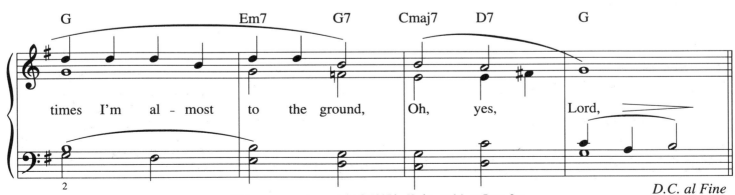

He's Got the Whole World in His Hands

Spiritual

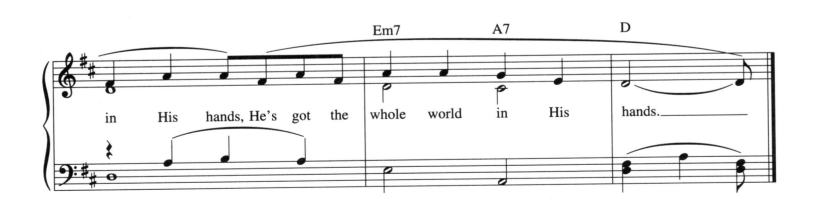

Short'nin' Bread

Traditional

When the Saints Come Marchin' In

Spirited walking tempo

Traditional

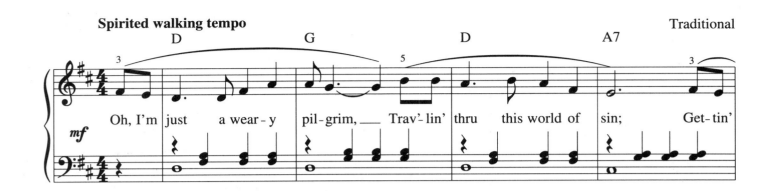

Oh, I'm just a wear-y pil-grim, ___ Trav'-lin' thru this world of sin; Get-tin'

read - y for the day ___ When the saints come march-in' in. ___ Oh, when the

saints ___ come march-in' in, When the saints come march-in' in, Lord, I

want to be in that num-ber, ___ When the saints come march - in' in.

I Love You Truly

Carrie Jacobs Bond
(1862–1946)

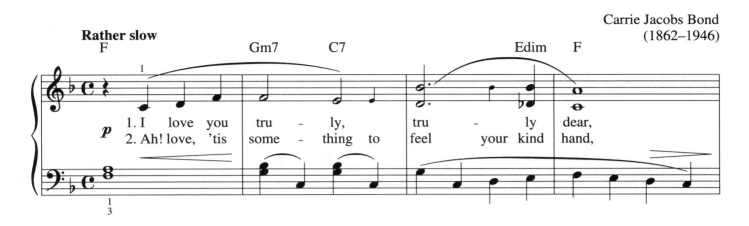

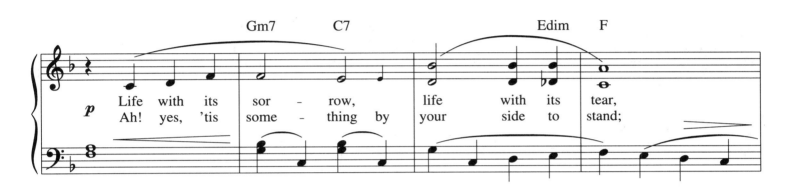

The Rosary

Robert Cameron Rodgers

Slowly

Ethelbert Nevin
(1862–1901)

The hours I spent with thee, dear heart, Are as a string of pearls to

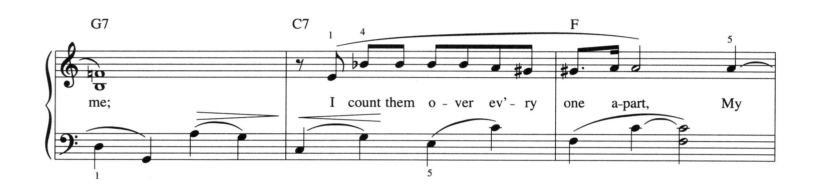

me; I count them o- ver ev'- ry one a-part, My

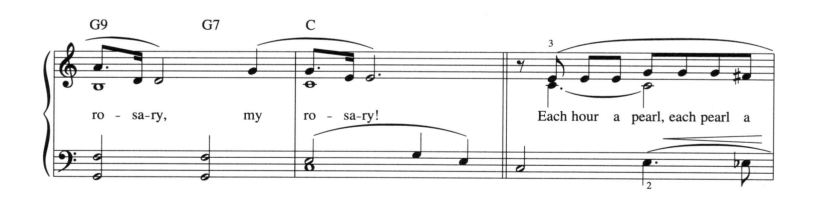

ro- sa-ry, my ro- sa-ry! Each hour a pearl, each pearl a

pray'r To still a heart in ab- sence wrung:

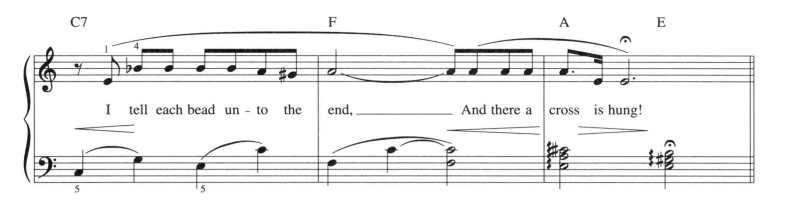

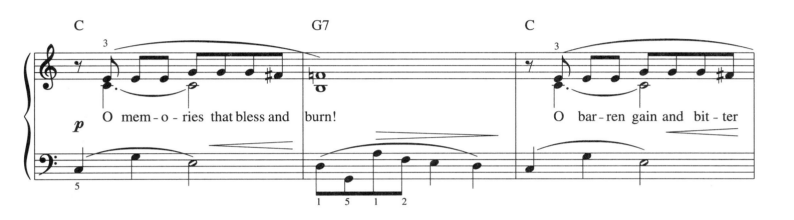

Mighty Lak' A Rose

Ethelbert Nevin

Slowly and gently

p Sweet - est lit - tle fel - ler, Ev'- ry -bod- y knows; Dun - no what to call him, But he's

might - y lak' a rose! Look - in' at his Mam- my With eyes so shin - y blue,

Make you think that heav -'n ___ is com-in' close to you! W'en he's there a- sleep - in',

Fine

In his li'l ___ place, Think I see the an - gels Look in'- thro' the lace;

W'en the dark is fall - in' W'en the shad ows- creep, Then they come on tip-toe To kiss-'im in his sleep.

rit.

D.C. al Fine

At Dawning

Nell Richmond Eberhart

Charles Wakefield Cadman
(1881–1946)

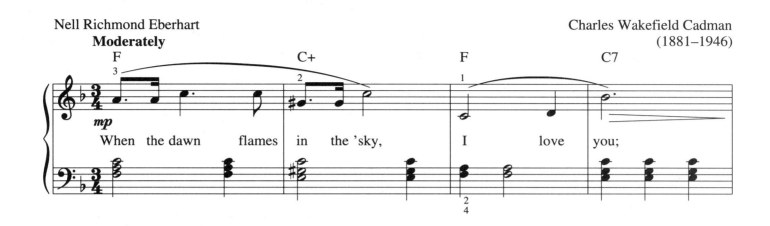

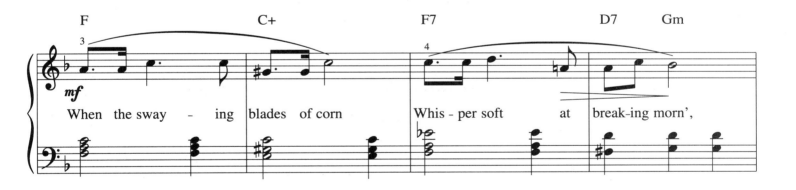

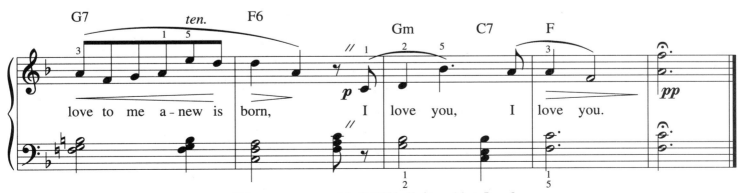

Oh Promise Me

Clement Scott

Reginald De Koven

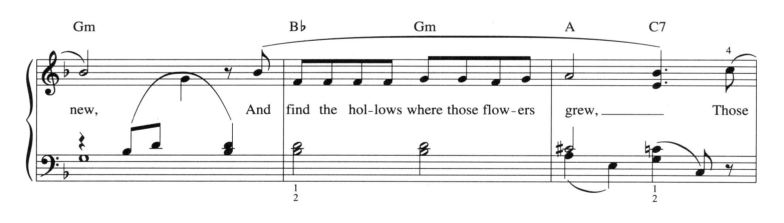

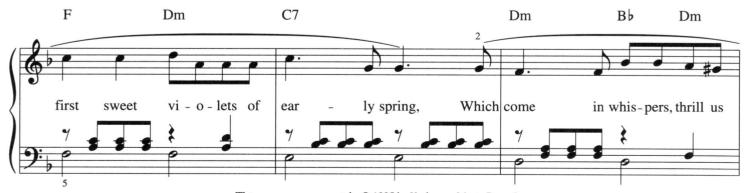

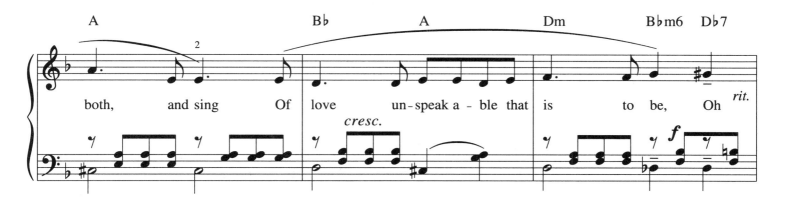

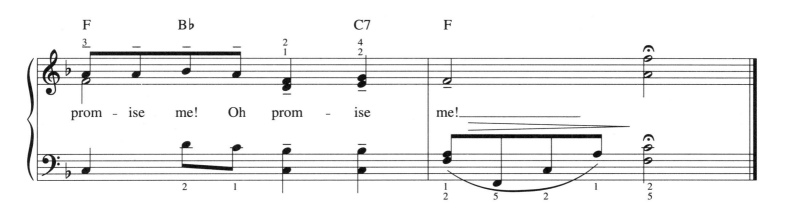

Carry Me Back to Old Virginny

Moderately slow

James A. Bland
(1854–1911)

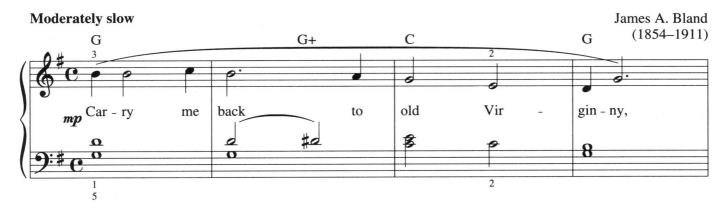

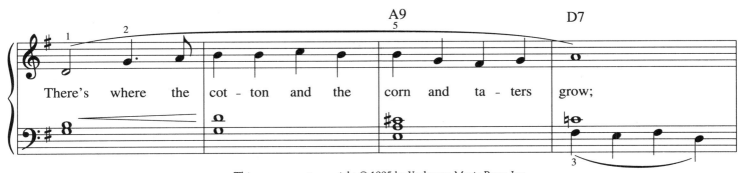

St. Louis Blues

With a slow, heavy beat

W.C. Handy
(1873–1958)

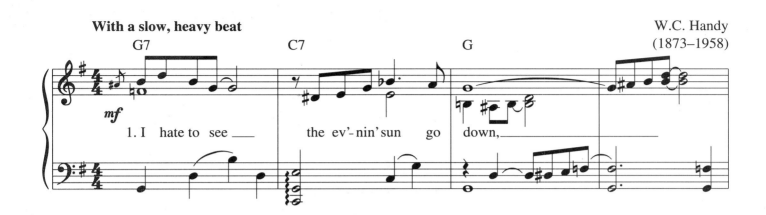

1. I hate to see ___ the ev'-nin' sun go down, ___

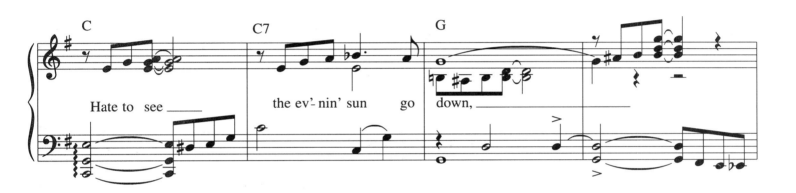

Hate to see ___ the ev'-nin' sun go down, ___

'Cause my ba-by, ___ he done left this town. ___

Feel-in' to-mor-row like ___ I feel to-day, ___

57

Over There

George M. Cohan
(1878–1942)

Lively march tempo

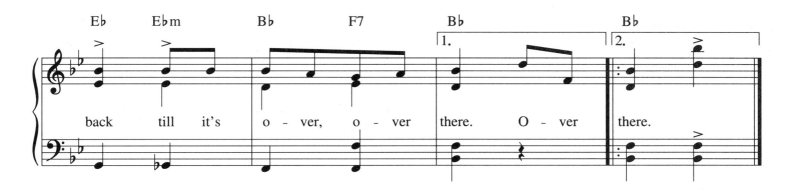

Yankee Doodle Dandy

George M. Cohan

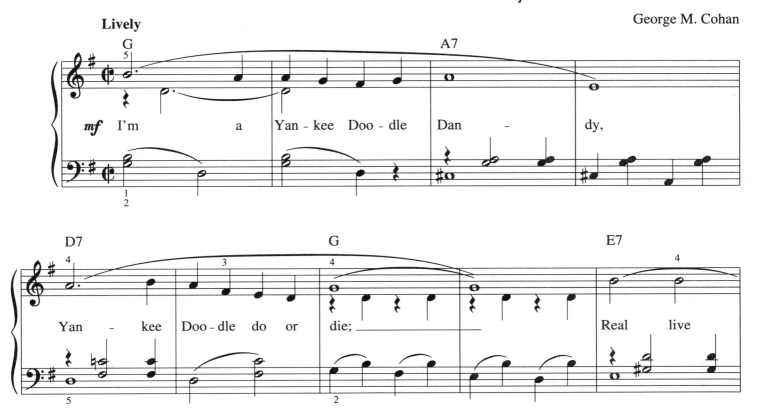

Will You Remember

Sweetheart

Rida Johnson Young

Sigmund Romberg
(1887–1951)

62

Toyland

from Babes in Toyland

Glen MacDonough

Victor Herbert
(1859–1924)

Slowly, dreamily

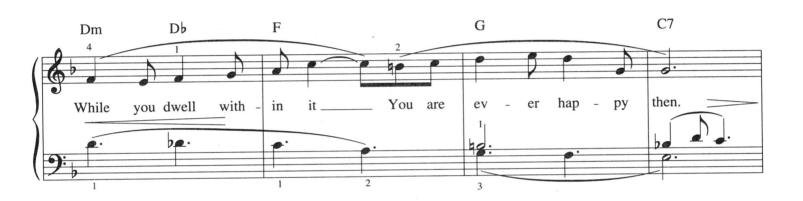

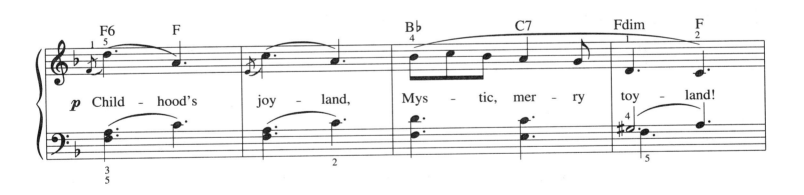

Sympathy Waltz

from The Firefly

Otto Harbach

Rudolf Friml
(1881–1972)

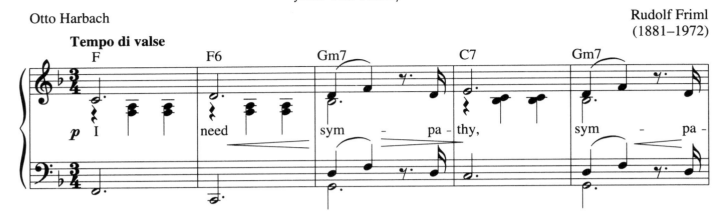

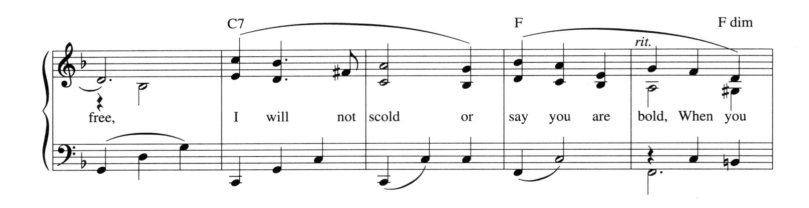

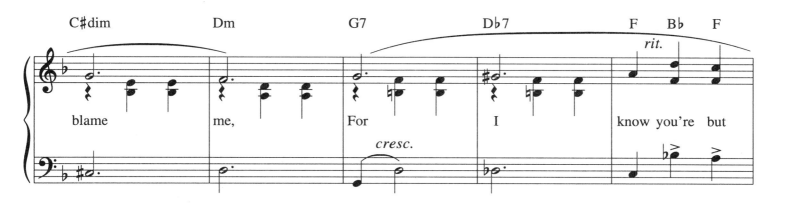

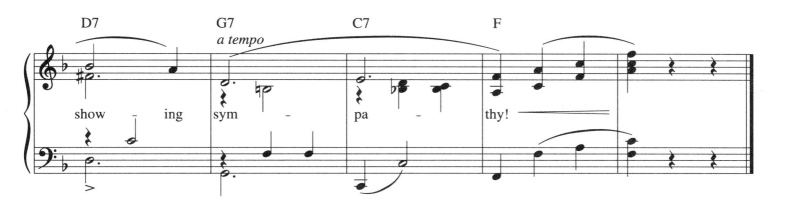

Thine Alone
from Eileen

Victor Herbert

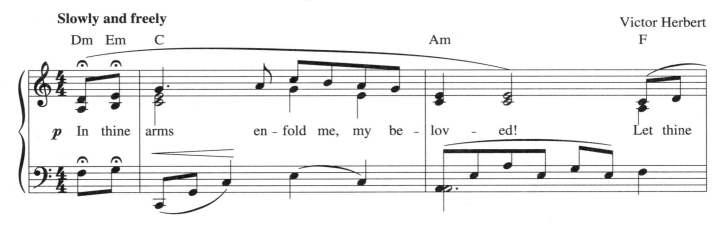

66

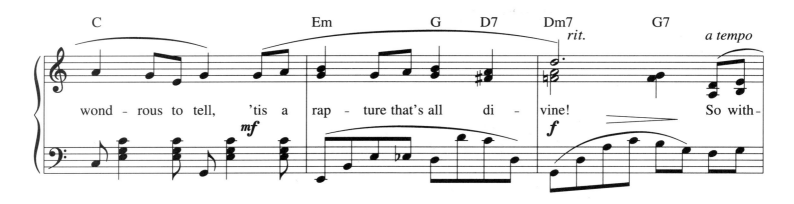

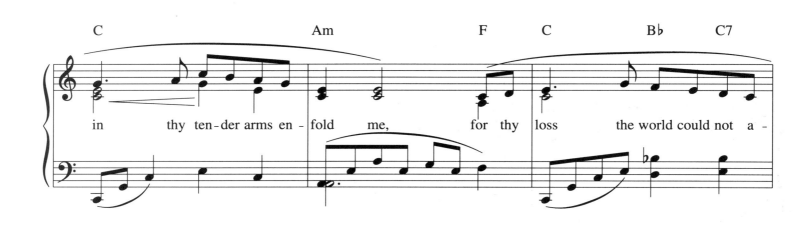

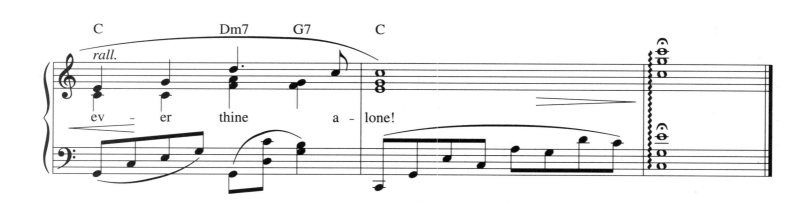

On the Road to Mandalay

Rudyard Kipling

Oley Speaks
(1874–1948)

By the old Moul-mein Pa - go - da look -in'

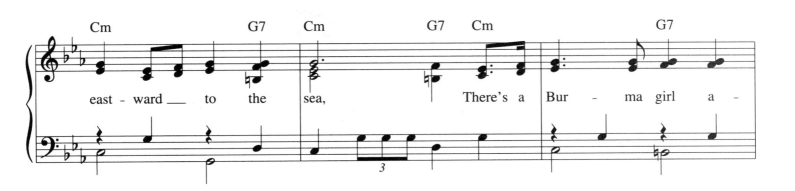

east - ward __ to the sea, There's a Bur - ma girl a -

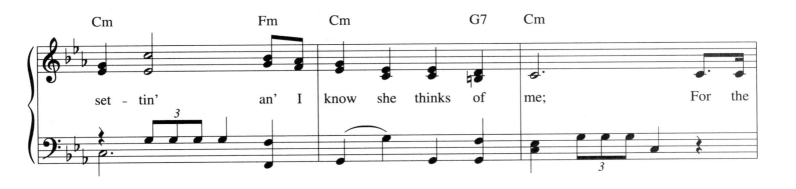

set - tin' an' I know she thinks of me; For the

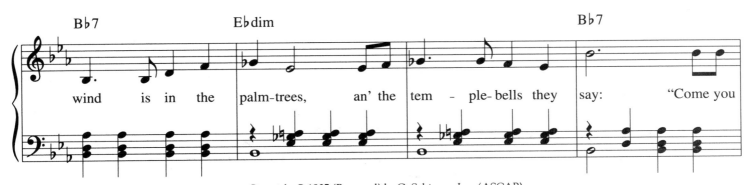

wind is in the palm-trees, an' the tem - ple-bells they say: "Come you

fly - in' fish - es play, An' the dawn comes up like thun - der out of

1.
Chi - na 'crost the bay.

2.
Chi - na 'crost the bay.

The Donkey Serenade

Bob Wright and Chet Forrest

Rudolf Friml

Con moto

There's a song in the

A Real Slow Drag

from the opera Treemonisha

Scott Joplin
(1868–1917)

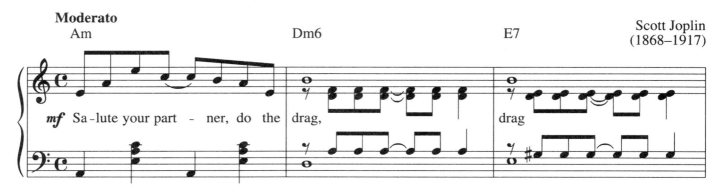

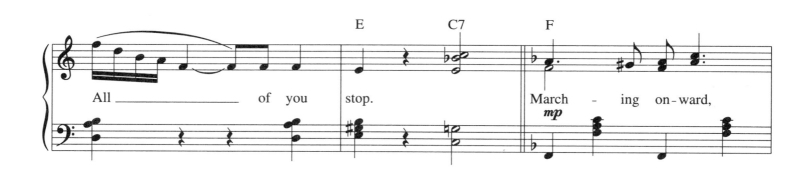

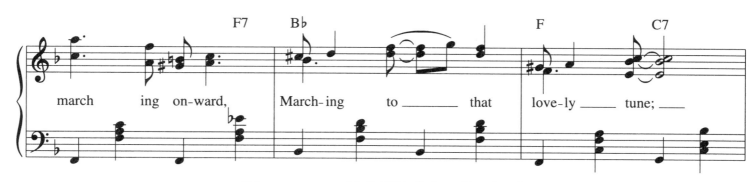

Alexander's Ragtime Band

Irving Berlin
(1888–1989)

Medium Bounce

Trees

Joyce Kilmer

Oscar Rasbach
(1888–1975)

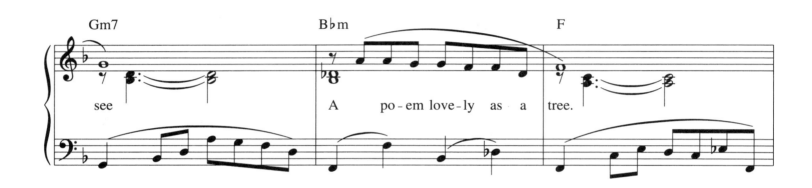

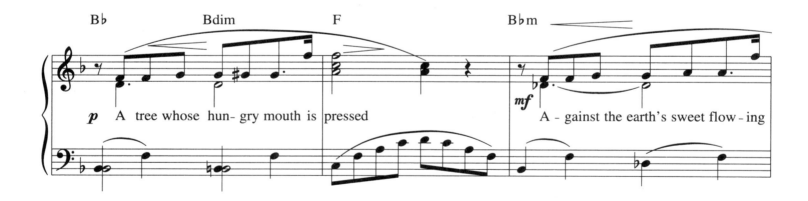

The Lord's Prayer

Matthew 6 : 9-13

Albert Hay Malotte
(1895–1964)

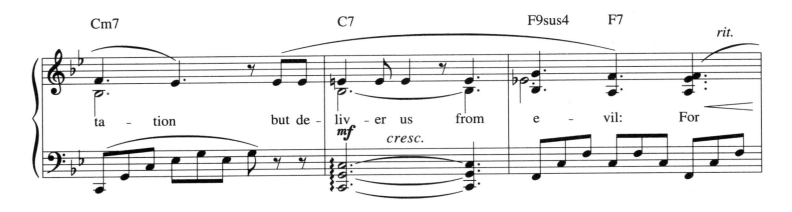

ta - tion but de - liv - er us from e - vil: For

poco meno mosso, sonoramente

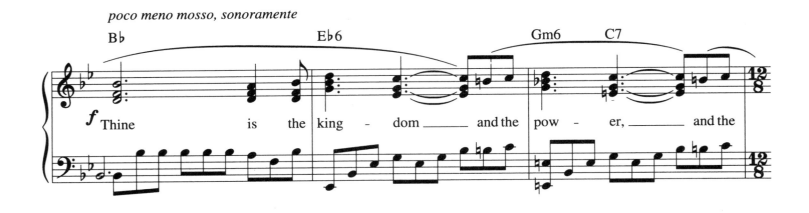

Thine is the king - dom _____ and the pow - er, _____ and the

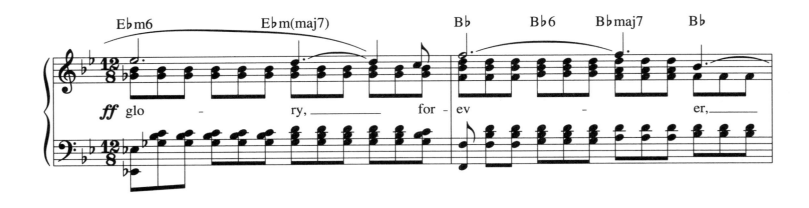

glo - ry, _____ for - ev - er, _____

Tempo I

A - men.